Hillytown Bis

CW01099463

Hillytown Biscuit Church

written and illustrated by
Ruth Whiter

CHRIS✝IAN
education

Published by Christian Education Publications
1020 Bristol Road
Selly Oak
Birmingham
B29 6LB

First published 2008.

ISBN 978-1-905893-15-7

British Library Cataloguing in Publication Data:
A catalogue record for this book is available from the British Library.

Printed and bound in the UK by Biddles Ltd, 24 Rollesby Road, Hardwicke Industrial Estate, Kings Lynn, Norfolk, PE30 4LS

Acknowledgements

The scripture quotation on p.45 is from the HOLY BIBLE, NEW INTERNATIONAL VERSION®. NIV®. © 1973, 1978, 1984 by International Bible Society. Used by permission of Zondervan. All rights reserved.

The scripture quotations on pp.67 and 79 are from the *Holy Bible, New Living Translation*, copyright © 1996. Used by permission of Tyndale House Publishers, Inc, Wheaton, Illinois 60189. All rights reserved.

For permission to reproduce the lyrics:

'Let there be love shared among us' (p.7) by Dave Bilbrough © 1979 Thankyou Music; 'The splendour of the king' (p.86) by Chris Tomlin, Jesse Reeves, and Ed Cash © 2004 worshiptogether.com Songs/sixsteps Music/kingswaysongs. com & Alletrop Music CopyCare; 'The lord's my shepherd' (pp.113-14) by Stuart Townend © 1996 Thankyou Music; all copyright adm. by worshiptogether.com songs excl. UK & Europe, adm. by kingswaysongs.com: tym@kingsway.co.uk.

To both Cynthias

Contents

Sunday 4 February
Aniela

'Nancy! I have asked you three times to get your shoes on!'

I was sliding down the banister. It was obvious that my mum and dad would spend at least another five minutes finding keys, putting collection money in little envelopes, grabbing spare clothes for Isaac, looking for photocopied sheets, and both checking the back door was locked, before we'd set off. There was plenty of time for shoes.

My parents often get cross before we go to church, because of the rush. They sometimes get cross after church too, but for different reasons, maybe because of something someone has said to them. But in between, while we're there, we mostly have fun.

We call it Hillytown Biscuit Church. That isn't its real name – we call it that because there are always a lot of biscuits. During the service, they are out on a plate, covered by a tea towel, in the foyer at the back. If you're very young and you cry a lot you might get one sneaked out during the service. Otherwise, if you're older, you need to run as fast as you can as soon as Sunday School is over, down the stairs, through about four doors, and carefully dodge chatting grown-ups in the aisle to get to the chocolate ones before they all go.

There are only a few children at our church. Very often, in Sunday School, there are only four of us: Rob, the minister's son, who's fourteen and is supposed to be a helper now; me, Nancy (I'm eight and three quarters); my brother Isaac (two and a half); and Kim, who's not much bigger than him. The only person close to my age is Jake, who comes when he's staying with his dad. But he's a year below me at school and I don't really talk to him.

Or rather, this is how it was, before the Polish family came. We have a minister at Hillytown Biscuit Church. As I said, he's Rob's dad. His name is Paul, and he stands at the front and does most of the talking and praying, and tells everyone what to sing next. Paul and Rob look the same, they're thin and pale, they wear metal-rimmed glasses, and their hair usually needs cutting. Paul once had a wife, Rob's mum, but she died when Rob was very small.

Well, my mum had explained to me that there was a man from Poland who was learning to be a church minister, and he was going to help Paul for one year. His family were going to live here too. She had told me that there was a boy who was about ten, and a girl who was exactly the same age as me.

When we arrived at church, I saw the new family straight away. The boy was wearing a suit with a tie, like a man going to work, and his sister had a dark red dress on, all velvety with lace at the edges. I might have worn a dress like that for parties when I was about five. She had long, curly, yellow hair, held back with a fat velvet band. I would have liked to look at her more, but I knew what was coming. My mum would already be thinking about the possibility of my managing to say hello. I kept walking.

Through the church, through a side door, then another door, down the steps to the basement and through the toddler group storeroom, to my favourite place in the building. Inside an old peely door is the boiler room. It's dark in there; the light switch doesn't work. It's warm, and there's a ticking sound, and an echoey dripping sound, and lots of dark, old, dusty, cobwebby, warm pipes. There are pipes going from the floor to the ceiling, pipes going right across the middle of the room, and pipes that go up and then bend off in different directions, like a magical machine. When you touch them, rusty flaky dust comes off on your fingers. And there's been one tea towel hanging over a pipe to dry for as long as I can remember, which must be at least *five years*. I love it. It's always been a good place to hide until the service begins.

Of course my parents know I come here. I've been doing it as long as I can remember. When I was much younger, they would turn up after a few minutes. I would hang on to the pipes, they would pull me off, and sometimes my dad would carry me into church. Now, I can tell the difference between the sound of the music group practising, and the sound of the first song in the actual service. If I make my way up to church as soon as that happens, no one seems to mind, and I don't have to say hello to anyone at all.

I'd managed to do another job after I got my shoes on. In my coat pocket were three little crusts, cut from

Isaac's toast, that had still been on the kitchen table just before we left. I pulled these out now, and crouched down on the little concrete steps. There's a lower area in the floor of the boiler room where the actual boiler sits, and once or twice, I'd seen a tiny grey mouse flash by down there. I'd been trying to remember to bring food for a couple of weeks. Perhaps if I sat very still, the mouse would come and eat, and I could watch him for longer.

It wasn't a long enough wait, this time. The music practice had already stopped, everything had gone quiet, and then the drums and the bass guitar began to thump above my head. It was time to go. I left the crusts, crept to the door, and closed it behind me.

Back upstairs, I sat down next to my dad, who was standing up, singing and swinging Isaac from side to side in his arms. Mum was playing with the music group. She'd been doing this for a few weeks, just playing with one or two fingers on the keyboard. She only started learning to play a year ago, when I started my piano lessons. While everyone was still singing, Dad stopped, and sat down, Isaac landing on his knee. He leaned over to me and explained that the new girl's name was Aniela, and the way you said it was *Anyel- la*. The Polish family was sitting near the front, and I could see Aniela's hair, and sometimes the edge of her face, smiling, when she turned to her brother or mother. I whispered the name to myself – An*yella*, An*yella*, An*yella*. It was a good name, I thought, because Aniela's hair was very yellow indeed.

The first song finished. Paul asked his new helper and his new helper's wife to come up on the stage with him. He told us a bit about them. The man's name was Darek and his wife was Magda. They were dressed as if they were at a wedding. Magda had yellow hair too, but short and wavy and all in the right place. Paul told us that they were going to help with our Easter Club. Then Paul put one hand on Darek's shoulder, and the other hand on Magda's, and prayed for them.

Then there was a surprise. Without anyone saying anything, Aniela and her brother, whose name was Daniel, walked onto the stage all by themselves and stood behind one of the microphones. Their dad wiggled the microphone so that it was low enough, and they began to sing. No one played any music; no grown-up waved about or even nodded to encourage them to begin. They sang a song in Polish, so we couldn't understand it, but they did it very well. We thought it was over, and clapped.

But then the big boy, Daniel, went over to my

mum at her keyboard and asked her something. She jumped up, a bit flustered, and moved away, and he sat down on her stool. Mum hovered at the edge of the stage, not sure what to do, because the rest of the music group were still there in their places.

Daniel began to play. He used all his fingers, and the keyboard sounded completely different. Aniela sang, on her own now, and in English. She sang a song we knew, although it's not one children usually sing. It goes:

> *Let there be love shared among us,*
> *Let there be love in our eyes,*
> *May now your love sweep this nation,*
> *Cause us O Lord, to arise...* *

They got to the end, and in the stunned silence, Aniela lifted up her arms, like a conductor with an orchestra, and the whole congregation stood up, just like that. Daniel started the tune again, and everyone joined in as they sang the same song again. The sound was wonderful. People were singing better than usual because they were so amazed by Aniela and Daniel.

Aniela looked beautiful, standing so still, smiling out at everyone, with her glossy yellow hair, her party dress, and her big dark eyes open wide. I liked look-

*From 'Let there be love shared among us' by David Bilbrough© 1979 Thankyou Music.

ing at her. But there was a funny knot in my tummy.

Whenever Paul the minister wants to play a silly game, or the congregation needs children to show them the actions for a song, or an advent candle needs lighting, I get a little nudge. It could be Mum, or Dad, or my Sunday School teacher Beryl, whispering 'Go on Nancy, you go!' They always use very kind voices, but I will never ever *ever* go on the stage during a church service. In a church with so few children, everybody knows this. And that day I knew that while the grown-ups were enjoying Aniela's beautiful singing, at some point, they would have a little think about me.

They would be wondering how I could be the same age and yet be so different.

I watched Daniel do a little bow to Mum, who was still hovering at the edge of the stage, and I watched Mum pick her way through the cables and stands, back to her keyboard seat, because there was another song to sing now, before we went out for Sunday School.

Sunday 4 February
The Boiler Room

Aniela had learned to sing one English song, but she didn't really know how to speak the language yet. This, however, did not make her shy. She and her brother left the main service for Sunday School with the other children as if they had been doing it their whole lives. If Aniela did know an English word, she made sure she used it whenever she could, and if she didn't know the right word to say, she just smiled a big smile instead. On the way to the Sunday School room, Aniela jumped in front of Rob, and said 'Hell-ooo!'

as if it was a funny word. Then she did the same with Jake, and then with me. I just looked down. She stood there, her head on one side, waiting, smiling, not letting me carry on up the stairs.

'Come along, my dear,' said Beryl, and led her back in the right direction.

Beryl is our Sunday School teacher. She's quite a big lady, and she sits on a tiny Sunday School chair, a silky petticoat showing under her skirt. I'm not too shy with her. Her eyes move to each member of the class in turn as she tells us a story from the Bible. I'm sure we've heard them all before, but we listen anyway. She has a grown-up helper, apart from Rob, whose name is Gillian. She's quiet, and she's always fiddling with something. I often watch her squishing a giant ball of Blu-tack, dividing it and rolling it and making balls and sausages. Rob sits on another small chair, hanging over his guitar.

Beryl had known the new children were coming, and she had already written their names in the register, and on their worksheets, and on their take-home papers, and on the birthday chart on the wall, and even on the sticker charts she used to show who came every week. (She always gave Jake extra stickers, because he couldn't come when he was with his mum.)

She had also carefully chosen some work that was just colouring and no writing, so that Aniela and Daniel didn't need to write in English. Everyone had a word in bubble writing on a sheet of paper, which we could colour and decorate with patterns to make a sentence from the Bible. Then the whole sentence would go on the wall of the classroom.

When we sat at the table, Aniela drew her chair close to mine, and gave me a different smile from under her hair, which was an invitation to be friends. I gave her a tiny smile back, and carried on choosing my felt-tips. Aniela was beautiful, but I wasn't sure about her being so close. I chose light blue, orange, light green and yellow. Aniela dug her hand into the tin too, pulled out two Barbie pink pens, and gave one to me. I can't stand pink, and anyway, I know they don't work. I put mine back in the tin. Aniela gave it back to me. Well, I just wouldn't use it. I started slowly filling my letters with wavy lines and loopy lines and hearts and stars, and Aniela started copying me. Of course her pink pen didn't work, so she used all the same colours I did. Then Aniela had a go at reading my word. The first two letters were from her own name.

'An? An?' she tried.

'Anxious,' I explained.

'Anshuss,' repeated Aniela, and then pointed to her own sheet. She could manage her own word. 'Not!' she whispered, pointing to it. 'Not! Not!'

After Sunday School, I ran for the biscuits, and Aniela followed me. We were fast enough to get bourbons, which just about count as chocolate. My mum was nearby, talking to Magda. Aniela sidled up to her mother, who put her arm around her shoulders.

'This is Aniela, my mischievous one,' said Magda with a smile.

'Oh, yes, that was wonderful singing,' said my mum. 'She's so confident, isn't she! '

Then Magda looked past my mum and straight at me with a broad smile. She crouched down slightly, and asked me, 'And what is your name?'

I know I should be able to say 'Nancy', but when I'm asked, everything inside me tells me to run away, and the word is so far away from my mouth I could never make it happen. I looked round at the biscuit plate, checking what was left, leaving Aniela's mum in her crouched smiley position. Then I felt my mum's hand stroke my hair. 'This is Nancy,' she said, rescuing me. 'And my little boy is Isaac, over there with his dad.'

But it wasn't over.

'Hello Nancy,' said Aniela's mum, her smile just as big, her eyes still at my level and not moving up to talk to my mum.

'And what are you learning in your class today?'

She held her head, and half her body, at an angle, so that she could catch a reply. I looked down. She wasn't going to get one, even after I'd swallowed the rest of the biscuit.

I was quite glad when Aniela grabbed my arm and yanked me away. I ran with her back through the church, back out of the door that I use to get to the basement. Behind it there's a little room that has lots of cupboards built into the walls. Aniela stopped here. She skipped up to a cupboard, opened the door, and pulled out an old, old, hymn book. She flicked through the pages, sending up a puff of dust, and then dropped the book on the floor, and opened another cupboard. It was full of old glass vases, and fortunately she left these alone. In the next cupboard she found a stack of old board games, and she pulled out the entire pile and put them on the floor. I picked up the hymn book and put it back while Aniela began opening boxes. I imagined tiddlywinks and cards all over the floor and wondered if we could go somewhere else.

'Do you want to see my favourite place?' I asked. I don't know whether she understood that, but Aniela grinned. I picked up the games boxes and put them back in the cupboard. I let her follow me down the basement steps, through the toddler group storeroom, to the peely boiler room door. I opened it and led Aniela into the dark. Straight away, Aniela's hand tightened around mine, and I felt her stop and become stiff. She made a little girl's scared noise. I turned round.

'It's all right,' I said. 'I always come in here. It's not scary.'

She said something like '*payonch*'.

'What?'

'*Pająk*,' she repeated, and then made a sign, with all the fingers of one hand running up her other arm. I was confused. Could she possibly know about my mouse? Then Aniela grabbed my hand again, quite hard this time, and pulled me out of the boiler room. She started to run before I did, and I fell, tripping over a toddler group tricycle. Aniela found an English word she had already learned.

'Sorry! Sorry! Sorry!'

'It's OK,' I replied, rubbing my leg. 'What were you scared of?'

Aniela ignored my question. She put her hands on my shoulders and looked straight at me.

'Friend?' she asked.

I did like Aniela. But it was hard to tell what she was going to do next. I smiled.

'Come on,' I said. 'Let's get another biscuit.'

As we went back through church, Jake suddenly stopped in front of us. He had a birthday invitation for me, one of those big glossy cardboard ones from Flying Kidz. This was a bit of a surprise. Jake is a boy and a year younger than me. I would never have expected an invitation to his birthday, but when I looked at it, it was actually for me *and* Isaac *and* my mum and dad.

Jake turned to Aniela. 'You and Daniel, you're invited too,' he said, 'only we didn't have an invitation for you.'

I showed the invitation to my mum.

'It'll be Jake's dad organising the party,' she said. 'It's going to be a big do. I think he wants all his friends from church to be there. It's the weekend after next. I suppose we'll go.'

My mum hates Flying Kidz. It's partly a busy, dark, grubby restaurant, and partly a giant play area. I couldn't wait. There are enormous vertical slides that drop you into ball pools, and as Jake was going to be eight, hopefully the biggest ones would be open. I would never have thought of inviting Jake to my own party, and there would be a lot of children there I didn't know, but at least I would be with my new friend.

Aniela.

Sunday 11 February
The Baptistry

The next Sunday, I wanted to find something better, maybe some sunflower seeds, for my mouse friend. But Mum and Dad were still in the kitchen.

'We are going to church and *you* are going to play keyboards.' Dad's voice came out in short low bursts, as if he would rather shout.

'It's silly, I only volunteered because no one else could play!' Mum's voice was a suppressed whine.

Dad turned to me 'Nancy, get your shoes on. Have we got spare things for Isaac?'

There were quite a lot of different instruments in the music group at church. Sometimes there were three people playing different sorts of guitars, and loud drums, a flute, and a violin, and then there was Mum on the keyboard. Probably Daniel should do it instead of her now, at least for the beginning of the service, before we leave for Sunday School. She could still play after that.

I don't really sing while we're in church with the grown-ups. What I really like is the singing *in* Sunday School. This is Rob's special job – it's what he does to help. He chooses the songs and plays them on his guitar, and there are some we really like and sing really loud. Sometimes we get silly and sing things like 'Our dog is a great big dog', when it should be 'Our God'. This week, Daniel and Aniela's second week, we sang 'Be Bold! Be Strong! For the Lord your God is with you!' It doesn't need silly words, you can just shout and stomp and yell and shake your fist when it goes 'I am not afraid – NO! NO! NO!' It's actually one of Jake's favourites but he wasn't there to belt it out. We did a pretty good job anyway. Even Isaac and Kim were yelling and laughing by the end.

After singing, Beryl asked everyone for their news. Kim had brought her new wellies to show; Isaac told her his pirate sword was broken. I just shook my head when Beryl asked me, and Aniela and Daniel both said 'Hello, we are very pleased to meet you today.' Then Beryl said, 'Rob has some very exciting news for us today. Do you want to tell everyone what you're going to do, Rob?'

Rob, hunched over his guitar, his floppy hair over his face, cleared his throat. 'On the twenty-fifth of February I'm going to get baptised,' he mumbled.

'Isn't that wonderful?' said Beryl. No one spoke.

'Do you all know what Rob means?' Beryl asked. More silence.

'Would you like to tell them what that means, Rob?'

Rob's head moved a little closer to his feet, but I could still see his face turn redder. Beryl carried on for him.

'Rob has decided that he definitely believes in Jesus and wants to follow him for the rest of his life.'

I felt funny about her saying this. Beryl always talks about *us* following Jesus, but not about *Rob* doing it.

'So in two weeks' time we're going to have a special service at church, and Rob will go into the baptistry and go right under the water to show that his old life is over, and that he's starting a new life with Jesus.'

I was so surprised that I spoke. '*What* water?'

'The water in the pool at the front of church,' Beryl replied, as if this was obvious.

'*What* pool?'

'Well, on the stage, where Paul and the music group stand, if you move some of the carpet, and then lift up some wooden boards, there's a little pool, that's our baptistry. Surely you've seen it before? Let me think ... the last person to get baptised here was – I think it was Kim's mum, and that was before she was married, that must be five or six years ago. You would only have been two or three, Nancy. You might not remember. And Jake wasn't coming to church then. You remember, don't you, Rob?

'Yes, I do,' said Rob, a little less red in the face now.

'Well, then, it will be the first time any of you younger ones have seen a baptism. Isn't that exciting? What about you, Daniel and Aniela? Do you know about baptism?'

They just smiled, so Beryl drew a little picture of a big bath full of water, and a stick figure standing in it up to its waist. Then she drew an arrow to show where

the figure would go into the water.

'Oh, yes', said Daniel. 'In Poland we have this.'

After Sunday School I took a detour on my biscuit run. I couldn't resist climbing on to the stage in church, and sure enough, under the music stands and wires, there was a funny shaped separate piece of carpet. I stood on it and jumped, and then jumped on the normal carpet, and there was a difference. Something different was underneath. I have been exploring Hillytown Biscuit Church since I learned to walk, and here was something I had never found.

It should have been exciting to find out that there was something like a swimming pool underneath the music group. Instead, I could feel a new knot coming in my stomach.

I had listened to Beryl tell the same Bible stories and the same things about God loving me and being kind over and over again my whole life, and now, suddenly, there was something I hadn't heard before. I *had* heard of baptism: there were a couple of stories where Jesus or another man from the Bible were baptised in a river. That was in the Bible, a long time ago. Beryl was saying that if you wanted to believe in Jesus *now*, at Hillytown Biscuit Church, you had to go up on this stage during a service, with everyone watching, and then go under some water. Why? How long did you have to stay under? Where did the water come from? Was it cold, and did you wear your swimming costume? Did anyone ever drown?

Somebody took my hand. It was Aniela, and she had brought two biscuits. They were only digestives, but I was polite about that.

Saturday 17 February
The Ball Pool

The next Saturday, I arrived at Flying Kidz at the same time as Aniela and we went bananas. We threw ourselves down twisty slides, bumpy slides, inflatable slides and vertical drop slides. We squeezed breathlessly through padded vinyl rollers, raced across rope bridges, and flew through the air on a runway, swinging and banging, upside down and covered in plastic balls. When our parents got our attention to say the food had arrived, they all looked a little fraught. Aniela's family and mine were sharing a big, dark, sticky table. I'd asked for chicken nuggets from the kids' menu but they were a bit shrivelled and chewy. Aniela had copied me. I emptied two sachets of ketchup and hoped that would help me get enough of them down. Our parents were talking about church.

'I would very much like that Daniel plays in the music group.' This was Aniela's mum, Magda, who was on a diet and eating salad.

'Oh, yes... yes, definitely' said my mum. 'I only volunteered because no one else could play at the time. Daniel's a much better keyboard player.'

'Oh, Rachel, don't put yourself down,' my Dad sighed. Then there was a bit of a silence.

Then Aniela's dad, Darek, spoke.

'Rachel, we must talk with you soon about Easter Club. I heard you would be interested in helping.'

We had an Easter Club last year, in the mornings for one week of the Easter holidays. It was great. My mum was in charge and she had sock puppets called Simon Sock and Peter Sock – they were really funny. There were about six children from my school as well as the church kids. We played mad games that always got too rough.

I remembered having fun, and it made me want to get back to the slides.

I had eaten four nuggets and about six chips, and I didn't feel hungry any more. I pushed my chair back and slid off the seat. Magda looked up at me, her smile held quite tightly. She glanced at my mum, and then gave me a look with raised eyebrows and big waiting eyes. I slid away around the nearest corner.

'Nancy, are you sure you've had enough?' my mum called.

Then I heard my dad. 'Come on, eat a bit more than that, Nance!' I knew that when the food was as unhealthy as this, neither of them would force the issue, and I carried on moving away from the table and away from Magda's look. Then I heard Aniela, who learned new words every week, shout 'Wait!'

I peered back round the corner. Aniela was coming to join me. She had eaten faster than me, but there was still some food left on her plate. Her parents spoke in Polish but what they said was clearly much more firm, as if it was really bad to leave a few chicken nuggets uneaten. Darek, who was sitting next to her, put his hand on her shoulder so that she was lowered gently back to a sitting position, her lips set in a sulk. She started to eat again, watching me. I hopped about a bit. I looked at the slot machine I was standing next to. Then I very quietly moved back to the table, slipped back onto my chair, and soon I'd eaten everything else on my plate. When Aniela had finished, she asked something in Polish. I knew what it would be. Her mum nodded, she got up, and I just got up at the same time. I hate saying words that I'm supposed to say. Magda looked at me again.

'In Poland we would never leave the table without asking the parents.'

My mum said, 'Nancy, would you like to leave the table?'

I nodded. I began to move. But again, Magda wasn't going to change the subject.

'Well, then?' said Magda. 'You can say your own words?'

She just doesn't know me. Everyone else knows what I can't do. I had to ignore her and go, very quickly.

Five minutes later, when we arrived at the bottom of the twisty slide, there were Jake and Daniel in the ball pool, laughing.

'Look! Aniela! I do the baptism!' said Daniel. He stood with his arms crossed across his chest, closed his eyes, and fell straight back into the balls. Everyone automatically piled on and covered him with balls, laughing. 'Aniela, you do it!' he suggested. Aniela copied his fall, and everyone piled in again, getting a bit rougher this time, throwing more balls onto her until she kicked them all out of the way. Now it was a game.

I joined in covering Jake and then one of his friends with balls. 'This is what we do at church!' Jake said, and his friend said that was wicked.

Then Daniel turned to me and said, 'Nancy, you do the baptism!' and suddenly the knot in my stomach was back. I pretended I hadn't heard, and started to make my way out of the ball pool. This is never easy, and in this case the only exit was up lots of overlapping slippery green slopes at different angles, so you have to bend back on yourself to climb up. Aniela wanted the game to go on and came after me, grabbing my sleeve. 'No, I don't want to,' I said, and pulled myself onto the first green slope. Aniela grabbed my trousers and pulled hard. 'No!' I shouted, and kicked my legs sharply out of the way. My socked foot did swipe Aniela on the nose, but it was her own fault. I kept climbing. Through the rollers, across the bridge, down the big bouncy slide, through more balls, and then I made my way back to the even messier restaurant table. I didn't look at Aniela's mum, just at mine. 'I've got tummy ache,' I said.

'That's not surprising with all that throwing yourself about straight after your food,' she said.

Later, when my mum came to say goodnight, she had got herself ready for a little talk.

'Nancy, you're going to be nine soon. There are a few little words you really need to learn to say, even if you don't want to. I can't say them for you any more, you're just too tall and too clever.'

'Mum', I asked, 'Have you ever been baptised?'

'Oh ...' she answered, successfully distracted. 'Well, you see, the church I went to when I was growing up didn't baptise adults. I was baptised when I was a baby.'

'What?' I sat up in bed, my mind boggling.

'Not in a pool like they do at Hillytown. I had some water sprinkled on my head. My parents made promises that they would bring me up to believe in God and to trust Jesus, and they prayed that God would bless me and make me one of his children. Those prayers and promises came true for me, so I don't think I need to do it all again. I became part of God's family then, and I've just been learning more about him ever since. Some people call it christening.'

'Oh ...' Of course I'd heard of that. 'But why didn't you do that for me?'

'Well, we started going to Hillytown when you were a baby and they don't do infant baptism. We still had a service to say thank you for you and pray that we'd bring you up to know about God. But we wanted to let you make your own decision when you were old enough.'

'That's not fair. You can believe in Jesus just because somebody put a bit of water on your head when you didn't even know what you were doing, but I have to go on the stage and get in a pool and get pushed under the water in front of everyone, and I don't want to ever do that, it's not fair, why couldn't you have done it that other way for me?' I almost made myself cry.

'Oh, love, I can see it's a bit confusing. But you really don't need to think about it just now. You can get baptised whenever you're ready. You could wait until you're older than Rob. He's been asking his Dad if he can do it for years. I think Paul asked him to wait *until* he was fourteen. But Nancy, it doesn't make any difference, you can still believe in Jesus, you can still be part of God's family. Baptism is really just a way of showing everybody that you are. You'll be ready one day. But just now, Nancy, you need to try to do something much easier than that. You need to learn to say "hello", and "goodbye", and "please may I leave the table" when we're out with other people. Magda must think I'm a hopeless mother.'

'Please may I go to sleep now?'

'Of course you can. But will you try, Nancy?'

'Goodbye!'

'Goodnight, Nancy.'

Sunday 25 February
The Spider

On the morning of 25 February, the knot in my stomach was so big it really had become an ache. I said I didn't want to go to church.

'Oh, Nancy,' my mum sighed. 'It's the first baptism we've had at our church for years. Are you really going to make me miss it?'

'But my tummy really does hurt!'

'You didn't say that when you got up. Why do you tell me five minutes before we have to go?'

Dad crouched down to where I was curled up on the sofa.

'Do you feel sick?' he asked gently. I couldn't truthfully say that I did.

'It's a special day today,' he continued. 'It's really exciting at church when there's a baptism. It's a new person telling everyone that they believe in Jesus. And Rob is special to all of us. Mum and I would really, really, like to be there. Even if you're not feeling very well, do you think that if I took you in the car you might be OK?'

Mum thought this was ridiculous. The church was three streets away and Mum hated using the car if it was at all possible to walk somewhere. They began to get cross with each other.

'All right, all right, I'll go,' I interrupted, and got up to find my shoes. *Fifteen* minutes later, when Mum and Dad had their collection envelopes, and spare clothes for Isaac, and a baptismal card for Rob signed by everyone, then remembered the DVD they'd bought as a present for him, we all set off on foot. At least Mum didn't have to find any music. Daniel played the keyboard now, at least until Sunday School time. There were songs after we went out, Mum *could* still have played for those, but she didn't.

In church, a couple of adults were making sure the

smallest children stayed in the biscuit room (which meant Isaac and Kim, and Rob's little cousins who had come to see the baptism), because the baptistry was open and full, and they might fall in.

'They're being a bit over-anxious,' said Mum. I remembered that word from the first day I met Aniela. I remembered how to spell it.

No one stopped me walking through the church and having a little peep at the water. The baptistry was like a tiny swimming pool, with steps at both ends. The water wasn't deep, and you could perhaps swim three strokes from one end to the other. There were lots of plastic mats leading from one set of steps to a door, and there was something in the pool, a giant metal coil like the metal bit inside a kettle, standing in the water. There was a cable leading from the top of it, which was plugged in with the music group's amps and things. I saw all this as I passed, but I didn't stop. I went straight on, out of the door that didn't have plastic mats leading to it, and down to the boiler room.

'Over-anxious,' I kept saying to myself. 'Over-anxious.' That was what I felt like. That was the feeling in my tummy. I remembered the letters I had coloured in Sunday School, and I tried to remember the other words in the sentence. Aniela had coloured in 'not', and Isaac and Kim had scribbled over 'do' and 'be'. Do not be anxious.

I was anxious. I was over-anxious, because all I had to do was watch a big boy splash in a little pool. It should be funny. But it made me feel a different sort of funny. It just wasn't like everything else that people do. You ducked under water in the swimming pool. At church, you did things like singing and praying to God, and you cut and coloured and glued, and ate biscuits, and ran around the building until it was time to go home.

Beryl, and Mum and Dad, and Paul, had talked about believing in Jesus, and following Jesus, and giving your life to Jesus, for as long has I could remember. I knew that Jesus was God's son, but really he was actually God as well, and believing in him had always been an obvious thing, a nice thing too, because Jesus was the kindest and gentlest person who had ever lived and singing songs about him made me feel warm inside. Not anxious. Not like this.

I knew there were more words after 'Do not be anxious.' I couldn't remember what they were, but it was easy to guess, like one of those boring questions people ask children, the ones no children can be bothered to answer. The answer would be that if you're anxious you should ask God to help you. I sometimes get anxious if I think too much about talking to God, so I did it quickly.

'I'm anxious,' I whispered with my eyes closed. 'Please help me.'

Immediately, I jumped with fright. The door rattled. When it opened, there was Aniela. She stepped back into the light straight away. Something about the boiler room obviously still bothered her.

'Come on, come on, the water!' she urged, jumping up and down. Somehow, before the service had even started, she had got hold of two custard creams, and she held one of them towards me, and then shuffled backwards, giggling, tempting me out of the boiler room. She clearly didn't want to come in and get hold of my arm like she usually did. The biscuit worked, and being with Aniela made me feel better.

When we got to the church, the coiled metal thing, which had been heating the water, had gone, and the church was much busier than usual. Rob was sitting on the front row with his gran. He was wearing a school shirt and khaki trousers, and he couldn't sit still.

'Come on, come on!' Aniela repeated, and led me onto the stage and right up to the edge of the pool. We stood there, munching our biscuits, looking down at the water.

Then I saw something floating. It was a black blob with long trailing legs. What was it? Not my mousie. Just when I realised that it was actually a giant, long-legged spider, and before I had time to wonder how it got there, there was a terrific scream. The scream was right in my ear because it came from Aniela. She didn't run away. Instead, she grabbed me hard with both hands. She launched herself onto me as if I could protect her, pushing me forwards and off balance. There was nothing I could do. We fell forwards together, and a second later there was a mighty splash,

and a loud scream from the bigger-than-usual congregation.

It was confusing in the water. I bumped my knees and then my elbows, and it took a few seconds to find the bottom for my feet, but it was lovely and warm. Heaven knows what had become of the spider. By the time Aniela and I had managed to stand up, holding on to each other, everyone who could move quickly enough was around us on the stage, most of them with both hands clasped over their mouths. I sometimes do that when something terrible actually feels exciting. Aniela and I didn't cover our mouths. We just laughed and laughed and laughed.

Sunday 25 February
The Rainbow

We were in Paul's office. The plastic mats had made a path all the way from the baptistry to this room, where the gas fire had been on for a while so it felt like a cosy sitting room. There was a very old-fashioned tin bath, the sort you would see in a museum. My mum and Aniela's mum squeezed out our sopping wet clothes over it. There were loads of enormous warm white towels too, so you couldn't have found a better place to be completely wet.

Aniela's mum was cross. She said a lot of things to Aniela in Polish, holding her by the wrists and looking very closely into her eyes. Aniela protested, and I heard the funny word she had used that first time in the boiler room. Aniela's mum sighed sharply, and turned to my mum.

'Aniela is very frightened by the *pająk*', she explained.

'I think she means spiders,' I suggested.

'Yes, yes, you are right, Nancy. The spiders. Even sometimes, if there is a room where the spiders might possibly be, she will not go in there. It is very silly, there is nothing else in the world that she is afraid of.'

She turned to Aniela and carried on scolding in Polish. Then she slowly said some English words, and repeated them. Aniela turned to me very seriously and said the same words again:

'I am sorry I pulled you in water, Nancy.'

'That's all right,' I said. I looked at my mum, who was quietly smiling. I felt happy. The knot in my tummy had mysteriously disappeared.

I had to wear Isaac's spare clothes. I'm thin, so I can get them on, but they became cut-off trousers and a crop top. Everyone wondered what Aniela could wear. She stayed wrapped in an enormous white towel, snuggled in Paul's office armchair until we discovered that Rob had brought two sets of clothes to change into, because he wasn't sure what he would feel like wearing after the baptism. Rob's cut off trousers, with the elasticated toggles pulled tight, worked perfectly, and she had a t-shirt down to her knees.

Eventually, Paul, Rob, Darek, my dad, Isaac and Beryl all came into the cosy office, laughing and ignoring the very late service, which hadn't even started. Only Magda seemed cross, and she was keeping that hidden now.

'I'm glad you spotted that spider,' Paul said. 'I think Rob would have screamed too – he's terrified of them!'

Rob changed the subject quickly.

'Are Aniela and Nancy baptised now?' he asked his dad.

'I think Aniela and Nancy might want to have another go when they're older,' Paul replied.

Well, he might be right. It didn't seem quite such a scary idea any more.

And next time I felt anxious, I would certainly tell God about it. He might make something amazing happen every time.

The service, when it finally began, was great. We

didn't go to Sunday School at all, and it wasn't even boring. There was lots of singing, with Daniel playing keyboard, and the songs were all Rob's favourites, which are my favourites too. Before the baptism Paul said that people who are getting baptised usually tell everyone how they came to believe in Jesus. There are lots of ways of doing this, and Rob wanted to do it by singing a song. He had written the song himself, he played it on his guitar, and the words were typed out on the big screen just as if it was a real church song. It went like this:

Sometimes I feel like I'm not good enough
You are a diamond
And I'm a bit rough
Sometimes I feel shy
So I act like a fool
And I don't talk about you
To my friends at school.

But then I remember
Just what you did
You died on a cross
And your friends they all hid.
And though I don't understand
Why this should be

I've known now for ages
You did it for me.

It was hard to hear what Rob was singing, but I could read the words on the screen. Rob knew that God was there, and I knew it too because he'd heard me in the boiler room. It all gave me a new feeling in my tummy. Not a knot. Maybe a big bow instead. Maybe a rainbow.

Paul and Rob both took their shoes and socks off. Paul made his way carefully down the steps, and then smiled at Rob, who was putting his guitar on its stand. Beryl got onto the stage, and stood on the plastic mats, holding yet another big towel. I could see tears in her eyes. She went up to Rob and took his glasses from him.

My mum put her arm around me. Paul held Rob's hand as he stepped into the water, and then showed him how to stand with his arms crossed, just like Daniel had done in the ball pool. He asked Rob a couple of questions about whether he believed in Jesus. Rob answered 'I do'.

Then Paul said 'I baptise you in the name of the Father, the Son, and the Holy Spirit.' When he said 'Father', Paul was lowering Rob into the pool. When

he said 'Son', he was under the water. When he said
'Spirit', he was coming up again. And that was that.

After Paul and Rob got dry, Paul read something
from the Bible. It was amazing! It was that very same
bit, the verse we did in bubble writing. I recognised it
when he said 'do not be anxious'. My dad was reading along with his own Bible, and when Paul finished
reading, I stopped my dad from shutting the book and
took it from him. He looked at me with a nice sort of
surprise. I scanned around the four columns of small
writing, and spotted it.

This is what it said:

> *Do not be anxious about anything, but in everything, by prayer and petition, with thanksgiving, present your requests to God. And the peace of God, which passes all understanding, will guard your hearts and your minds in Christ Jesus.**

The peace of God. Maybe that's what the rainbow feeling was! I wanted to be able to find this bit again. And I do know how you find things in the Bible. You need to know what book it's in, and this page said Philippians at the top. That's the book, and that's what you can find in the contents. You need to know the chapter, which is the big numbers you get every now and again, and what verse, which is the little numbers that are at the beginning of a lot of the sentences. The big number for this verse is 4, so it's chapter 4, and the little number is 6, so it's Philippians chapter 4 verse 6. That's what I need to remember.

We didn't just have biscuits after that service. We had sandwiches and crisps and pizza and big bowls of salad, then trifle, chocolate cake and lemonade. Aniela and I ran around the building while the grown-ups

---

*The Bible Nancy looked at in church was the *New International Version.*

talked and talked. I picked up a spare sandwich, beckoned for Aniela to follow me, and took it down to the basement for Mousie. When we got there, I put my finger on my lips. I opened the door and crept in, and then down the little steps. Aniela was behind me.

Then, suddenly, a light came on.

I blinked and looked round. Aniela sniggered. She had found the light switch, and it worked! Somebody must have changed the bulb. She stepped forward. She looked up, and craned her neck to see all four corners of the ceiling. She stepped in further, and peered in each corner of the floor. Finally, she checked behind the peely door.

'I don't think there are any spiders here,' I said. 'I've never seen one. I'm waiting for my mouse.' I curled up my hands and held them in front of my nose, and said 'eek eek'. 'Mouse!' I repeated. We giggled. 'Eek eek mouse,' said Aniela. She came and crouched on the step next to me, still looking around herself every now and again. We were really quiet, but no mouse came. Then it started to get boring. There was a pipe across the middle of the room, going to the boiler, and Aniela had a little swing on it. This made me want to show Aniela what I could do. I pulled myself up and somersaulted over the pipe. I'd never done that in there before, and I was sure anyone who saw us would think it wasn't safe. Aniela had a go, and got stuck with her tummy over the pipe.

'Ayayay!' she shrieked. And at that moment, the door opened, and there were both our mothers.

'Aniela!' Magda shouted. She pulled her daughter off the pipe, took her by the wrist, and smacked her on the bottom, which made my mum and me jump. Aniela didn't cry, she just looked cross. When Magda had finished telling her what she thought, she turned to me.

'This is not a place to play,' she said firmly. 'You children should not come in here again. You understand?'

I was quiet. My mum was quiet too. We didn't know what to say. This was *my* boiler room.

We had been at church for hours and hours. It had been a happy day, but when we were walking home it was already four o'clock. Isaac had eaten too many sweets, I was grumpy about the boiler room, and my mum was grumpy about Easter Club. She was talking for ever to my dad in a high, whiney voice.

'Well if they don't want me to do the sock puppets, if that's not good enough for them, and they don't want me to play keyboards, and they don't need me to run any of the activities, well, I don't see why they're so keen that I help. And I don't know how they think they're going to get so many children coming. They don't realise it's different in this country. And they seem to think they'll get all the Sunday School children doing a pantomime. I don't think they know what that means, and have they even noticed how many children we have, and of course Nancy won't do anything like that ...'

I ran ahead, and tried to think about the rainbow feeling again.

Sunday 4 March
Lunch

This Sunday I planned to go straight to the boiler room as usual. Magda had said we couldn't, but my mum hadn't, and Magda would never guess I was there. I felt so cross with her. I had been hiding in the boiler room all my life, and I had never climbed on the pipes. Well, only that one time. And she hadn't seen that. Paul and Beryl and my parents had never stopped me hiding there. She had been at the church three weeks, and she was already inventing rules. The boiler room isn't a safe place to hide if *she* might come in, telling me off and expecting me to talk.

The trouble was, when we got to church, Aniela was waiting for me in the foyer. If she came down to the boiler room, it was obvious who would follow. She skipped around me, and put her hands on my shoulders again, saying 'My friend!' I pulled her arms down.

'I– I need the toilet,' I mumbled, and ran off through the church. I did want to play with Aniela, just not now. But when I looked behind me, there was the flash of yellow hair and dark red velvet, following me. So I had to go into the toilet. I sat in there for a while. After a minute, Aniela was outside the door, knocking softly.

'Nanceee! Nanceeee!' she called. 'Nancy home to-day!'

I pulled the big old chain to flush the toilet and opened the door. 'What?' I asked.

'Nanceeee!' she repeated. 'Nancy – ' she walked her fingers along her arm – 'Home – today!'

I was itching to get to the boiler room, at least for a minute. But then it happened. There was Magda, come to shepherd Aniela back to her seat in the church. She put one arm around her daughter and one around me.

'Hello Nancy, time to go into church now. And you are looking forward to our visit today, yes?'

What visit? I thought. But of course I said nothing. I walked faster to get out from under her arm, and sat next to my dad.

'Dad,' I whispered. He leaned down to hear.

'Why is Aniela's mum talking about a visit?'

'Eh? What's that?'

'Aniela's mum was talking about me looking forward to a visit today.'

'Who's doing the visiting?'

I would have said that was what I didn't know, but my mum suddenly gasped, her hands in front of her face as if someone had fallen in the baptistry again. Then she said a word no one ever says at church. And some people heard it, because they went quiet. Then my mum spoke in a hoarse whisper.

'I asked the Polish family to come round for lunch today to talk about Easter Club,' she said, 'and I've completely forgotten all about it!'

After a moment, the people who were quiet started talking again. Mum and Dad urgently discussed the mess in the kitchen, the dirty bathroom, the toys on the floor, the absence of food in the house. Then, before they'd decided whether some sausages could be defrosted, there was Magda, putting herself on an empty chair in front of my mum.

'Rachel, I have heard that lunch may be difficult for you. So don't worry. You can have lunch at my home. It will be no problem. I can make lovely meal for everyone.'

Mum just stared. Dad protested that it would be very short notice for her, it would be too much trouble –

'It is no trouble at all, my dears. You will all come after church. No trouble.'

My mum looked as though she had frozen.

I didn't like Magda. But would I like to go to Aniela's house? Yes, I would.

By the way, we did sneak to the boiler room after the service. And we did somersault over the pipe. We just didn't stay too long.

Aniela doesn't live in a house, she lives in a block of flats. We had to go home and get our car to get there, it's quite a long way. You go through some big metal doors into a hallway that's a bit smelly, and there's a lift and stairs. I thought it was great to have your own

52

lift, but Aniela grabbed me again and made me follow her up the stairs. Up, and up, and up. She lives on the *fifth* floor. There's another hallway that smells like cats, and then Aniela's door. We caught up with the others just as they were going in. Inside, the flat is quite big and very tidy. There's one big room with armchairs and a very small TV sitting on top of a cardboard box. There's a shiny wooden table and chairs, and a new-looking light-coloured carpet.

Aniela took me to see her room, which is tiny, and the bed is the only thing you can see in there, until you open a cupboard in the wall. Aniela's clothes, and quite a lot of soft toys, are all in there. We could both fit in the cupboard too. We sat in the dark and Aniela told me the names of her toys, which are all Polish names of course. I tried to say them back to her, but she laughed every time I tried. Aniela's English was getting better all the time, but we still just talked one word at a time. When we ran out of words to say, Aniela rested her head on my shoulder and we just sat there, cosy and dark, stroking her toy animals.

Then, from behind the wall, I heard mum call out 'Oh, Isaac!' We went to see what he'd done, which was a wee on Magda's clean cream-coloured sofa. And although we'd taken spare clothes to church, for some reason we didn't have them now. There was a lot of fuss because the sofa doesn't belong to Darek and Magda. They are borrowing this flat, and Magda wasn't sure whether you could wash the cushion covers. Isaac came back to Aniela's room with us to see if there was anything he could wear, which could really only be a t-shirt that would cover him like a dress.

While we chose one for him, Isaac started getting Aniela's soft toys out of the cupboard and arranging them on the bed. He put them in rows, facing her pillow.

'They're at Biscuit Church,' he said.

'*Biscuit* Church!' Aniela repeated.

So we played a game with Isaac. We chose a skinny light-brown teddy to be the minister, and a smaller teddy to play the guitar, which was a pen Aniela found. We found a fat rabbit in a flowery dress and bonnet to be the Sunday School teacher, and we sat all the littlest animals with her. We made a gap down the middle of the bed for the aisle, and because some animals couldn't sit up by themselves, we rolled up Aniela's trousers and tops from the cupboard, and made long seats they could lean on. It was great, and we didn't need words: we knew between us exactly what everything was meant to be. Isaac wandered off after a while, and Aniela and I just carried on.

Our service started, and then I did have to do most of the talking, pretending I was Paul welcoming everyone. There was a golden fluffy dog with a bow on its head, and I made it come to the front and sing 'Let there be love shared among us'. This time, really, it was me singing, instead of Aniela!

Then Aniela disappeared. While she was gone I put a little brown mouse on the stage with the fluffy dog. Aniela came back, and I moved both of them quickly back to their seats. She was carrying a big round biscuit tin. It looked strangely heavy for her, until I saw that it was full of water. She looked at the bed, put the tin down on the floor, dashed out again, and returned with three towels. She laid one across the front of our church, and then carefully laid the tin on top. She laid the other two towels at the sides where there was still a bit of space. Then she took the teddy minister and the teddy guitarist and made them walk up to the biscuit tin baptistry and jump in. The teddy guitarist was baptised and placed on one of the towels. I picked him up again because he really needed a bit of a squeeze if her bed wasn't going to get wet.

I took hold of the teddy minister, and put on his voice: 'Is there anyone else here today who would like to be baptised?'

And there was. One by one, each of Aniela's toys came forward. When Isaac came back, he wanted to have a go, and of course he wasn't as careful as us. Then Daniel appeared.

'Cool!' he said, and joined in, inventing a sort of baptism where you dropped in from a greater height. Most of the water in the baptistry had disappeared, and Daniel took the tin to the bathroom and refilled it. There were wet toys all over the bed. Soon Isaac's borrowed t-shirt was wet too. My sleeves and my knees were wet. The towels were wet. I lifted one, and — underneath — the bed was completely drenched.

'I think we should stop,' I said. And just then, Magda opened the door.

Magda's Polish exclamations were loud enough to bring my mum running in seconds. She looked worried even before she could have seen what we were doing. And to my great shock, she reached in, grabbed me by the wrist, pulled me out of the tiny bedroom, and, still holding me far too tightly, she *smacked* me. Just as she'd seen Magda do. But for her, it was the first time ever. I couldn't believe it. I crumpled into tears. I couldn't even start to say that Aniela had got the water, that the boys had made most of the mess. I was crouching in a heap, mum's hand still around my wrist.

Then her voice came, angry and upset and hoarse, because she was crying too:

'WE — ARE GOING HOME – NOW'

'But Rachel, the stew is ready ...'

'WE — ARE GOING HOME – NOW!'

It was hard to say how this had all happened, but once we had started going home, we couldn't stop, even though Isaac had nothing dry to wear and the food was ready. Magda and Darek tried a little bit to persuade my mum to change her mind, but in a way her voice had been too loud and angry for the visit to be able to carry on. I couldn't believe this was my fault.

It was a cold day, and Isaac had to wear his own

damp smelly top out of the dirty clothes bag, and his coat around his bare legs. He screamed all the way home. I cried. Mum cried. We were all starving. At home, Dad made beans on toast which went all mushy and overcooked because he was arguing with my mum and not watching them. After I'd had some food I went to my room and lay on the bed, a horrible sick feeling in my tummy, while my parents carried on talking. Between us, we had made some sort of awful mess that you couldn't clear up. I wasn't even sure what the mess was.

Soon Isaac wandered in, still half dressed, and I took him to his room and found some pants and trousers for him. We did a couple of jigsaws together. Then there were footsteps on the stairs and my dad came in.

He knelt down and put his arm around my shoulders.

'Nancy,' he said gently. 'You know it wasn't only what you did that made Mum cross.'

'What did I even do? Aniela got that water and Daniel and Isaac got most of it on the bed—'

'No, I mean, it wasn't all about the bed. Your mum was a bit wound up before that.'

'Why?'

'Oh, it's hard to explain. She's got a bit stressed about Easter Club, and about Magda ...'

'But she smacked me!'

'I know. She shouldn't have done that. There aren't any excuses for that. She's really, really sorry.'

My mum did say sorry later on. And then no one mentioned that horrible Sunday again.

Monday came, I went to school, everything was normal. Saturday came, and then Sunday came again. I got my own breakfast and watched little kids' TV in my pyjamas with Isaac. It started to get boring and my feet started to feel cold. Then I noticed that the house was quiet, and calm. No one had told me to get dressed. No one had run up or down the stairs. I rolled off the sofa and wandered into the kitchen, where there's a clock.

It was a quarter past ten. Church starts at half past ten.

I wandered upstairs. Someone was in the shower. Then I found Mum, making her bed.

'Mum, it's quarter past ten,' I said.

She didn't seem to notice me. I spoke louder.

'Mum, it's time to go to church.'

'Oh ...' she stood up.

She looked only very slightly bothered about this.

'Mum, we're not even dressed!'

'Oh ... well. We're going to have a break from church today.'

'What?'

Dad came in, wearing his dressing gown.

'When did we ever not go to church?' I asked.

'Today,' said Dad. 'It's a lovely day. I thought we might drive to Crabb Hall, have lunch in the café. Do something different.'

Sometimes, you can't tell what parents are going to say next. If I ever brought home a birthday party invitation for eleven o'clock on a Sunday morning, my parents usually got really annoyed, because it was impossible to get me there without missing even a tiny bit of church. Usually it seemed as important as their jobs, as important as school. We had to rush to be ready and act as if we'd be told off if we were late. Which doesn't happen, of course.

And yet today, we got dressed slowly, and my parents made real coffee, and I had a muffin with chocolate spread, and Isaac watched more TV, and then we got in the car and drove to Crabb Hall. It was cold and sunny, and fairly quiet. There's an adventure playground there, with quite a good aerial runway. I had lots of turns on that, and ran alongside Isaac when he had a go, catching him before he bumped at the end. We had a nice lunch in the café. Isaac didn't really like anything, but I had macaroni cheese, which is one of my favourite things to eat. Then we walked through the gardens and the woods, and I ran ahead of the others so I could climb trees while they caught up. I wished Aniela was with me. My dad gave Isaac and me a pound each to spend in the gift shop. I looked for a toy mouse, but there wasn't one. Isaac bought a big hairy rubber spider, so I got one of those too. I could take it to church next week and make Aniela jump.

Sunday 18 March
Mother's Day

That Sunday was soon over, and then it was school again. I didn't think too much about my parents' strange behaviour, although I did look forward to seeing Aniela again. The weekend came again, and the next Sunday was Mother's Day. Dad got up with me, and helped me boil the kettle and make toast. I carried Mum's breakfast upstairs on a tray, together with cards we'd each made at school, and a chocolate orange. Mum was really pleased, and Isaac and I climbed into bed with her while she ate the toast.

Dad sat on the bed.

'Nancy,' he said. 'And Isaac — Mum and I were talking last night, and we think we're going to try going to a different church today.'

A horrible feeling jumped back into my tummy. It was the same horrible feeling that came during the cold crying car journey after not having lunch at Aniela's.

'You know my friend Jill,' Mum said. 'She goes to this really nice church where there are lots of children, lots of children your age, Nancy.'

I blurted out: 'I want to go to our Biscuit Church!'

'We just thought we'd see what it was like,' said Dad.

'No! I'm not going there. I want to go to our Biscuit Church! I want to see Aniela!'

'Just to try–' said Dad.

'I'm not going! I'm going to our Biscuit Church!' I shouted.

Then Mum stopped being calm.

'Nancy, a couple of weeks ago you were yelling because you didn't want to go to Hillytown. Are you just going to stop me doing whatever I want to do? Can't I try something I want to do just once? You don't even know what this church is like. You don't know whether you'll like it.'

I ran out of the room, into mine, and slammed the door.

What were they talking about? We *belonged* to Hillytown Biscuit Church. We didn't just *go* there, in the way you would go to visit Crabb Hall. The people at church knew us, they would expect us to be there. My mum and dad were pretending that it didn't matter, that *they* didn't matter to everyone else. I could see that it did matter. I could also see that my mum really really didn't want to have to talk to Magda, that she must feel stupid after getting so cross and leaving the flat. She didn't want to talk, and so she was hiding.

After a while, Mum came in, dressed, and said I needed to get ready now.

I said 'No. I'm not going.' When she came towards me I ran straight into her room and shut the door. There's a lock on her bedroom door and I pushed it in, knowing that would make her crosser than anything. Then I lay face down on their bed. Mum rattled the handle, and her voice got loud and rough.

'Nancy! Open the door!'

'NO!'

Then there was a bit of quiet, and she tried to talk calmly again.

'Nancy,' she said firmly. 'We are going in ten minutes, and you are coming with us. You need to get your clothes on and brush your teeth.'

'I'm not going,' I repeated.

'Yes you are,' she said, and then started to get cross again, as if I was doing this just to upset her. She rattled the door harder.

'Nancy, open the door! Open the door this minute!'

I put her pillow over my head as the screaming got higher. Then, I heard the muffled sound of Dad calming her down and both of them arguing their way down the stairs.

Downstairs, the argument got louder and louder, and I flattened myself on the bed and wished I could disappear. The horrible knot was in my tummy, and I wished I could go back to Hillytown Biscuit Church and sing with Rob and smile with Aniela and get the rainbow feeling.

Then I remembered how I got it. I sat up. My mum's big Bible was on her bedside table. I opened it and found the contents. Philippians started on page 1197. I found it, right near the back. Two pages later, there was chapter four. I found verse six. But it wasn't the same. I wondered if I'd remembered the wrong numbers, but I read it anyway. It said:

> *Don't worry about anything; instead, pray about everything. Tell God what you need, and thank him for all he has done. If you do this, you will experience God's peace, which is far more wonderful than the human mind can understand.**

It was different, but the same. Different words saying the same thing. And I already knew that what it said was true. If you tell God what you need, you get the rainbow feeling. You get a peace that you can't understand.

I closed my eyes.

'Dear God, this is what I need. I need to go to Hillytown Biscuit Church. I need to see Aniela. And I need my mum to stop being cross.'

Another thought crept into the back of my mind, a thought I wouldn't want to think myself. It was as if someone else had put it there. I had spoiled my mum's Mother's Day, and I needed to say sorry. I wasn't going to do that, but I did get up, get dressed

---

*This is how the verse appears in the *New Living Translation of the Bible*.

and brush my teeth. A minute later, it was quiet downstairs. Then there were footsteps. Then Dad came in, followed by Mum.

'Nancy,' Dad said gently. 'We've just been thinking about this. You are nearly nine. You could go to Sunday School without us. We're going to set off in the car in a minute. We could drop you at Hillytown, and then pick you up as soon as our service finishes.'

I was quiet for a few seconds. I looked at Mum.

'That's ridiculous,' I said. 'The church is only three streets away. I can walk there.'

No one said anything. I jumped off the bed, ran downstairs, put my shoes on, and then my coat. I used my hands to comb my hair a bit. I thought for a minute – there was nothing else I needed. I looked around, and the rest of the family were on the stairs. I think they were too surprised to speak. I felt calm, and I felt determined.

'I'll see you later,' I called, and opened the front door.

Mum was going to say something, but Dad interrupted.

'OK, Nancy, we'll see you later. Be careful.'

I closed the door behind me. The air was cool and fresh. It was a peaceful morning, and I felt peaceful too. I walked down the path, turned right, and walked around the long crescent-shaped road we live on. That takes a long time, but then half of the walk is done. I looked at the daffodils and crocuses in the front gardens, and listened to birds singing in the trees along the road. Then I turned right, and walked up the hill. There are only two roads to cross – one is halfway up the hill and the other is the road the church is actually on, where you turn right at the top. There are traffic lights and a green man there. I crossed the first road carefully, and when I got to the top I pressed the green man button even though there were no cars around. While I was waiting, a car did stop at the lights. I glanced at it quickly, and saw my dad inside. He, and my mum, and Isaac, were all looking at me. I pretended I hadn't seen them. The green man appeared, I crossed over, and then after a few more steps I was at the gates of the church. Just as I stepped through them, I heard the car set off.

I felt a little bit lonely then, but there was only one way I could go. One of the big black doors was open, and I walked up the path and stepped inside. After the black doors, there are white doors, and I had to push one of these open.

Then I was in the foyer, and there was Gillian, the Sunday School helper.

'Oh, hello, Nancy!'

Gillian's voice is soft and little, as if it has to come from far away inside her.

'Hello,' I replied, without even worrying about it. Gillian looked above and behind me, expecting someone else to appear, but she didn't mention my being alone.

'It's lovely to see you,' she said.

After the foyer there are more doors before you're inside church. There weren't many people in there, and looking round I could see no yellow hair and red velvet. I walked forward without looking at anyone too much. I didn't feel like going to the boiler room. I just sat down where we usually sit. Perhaps no one would notice me. Hopefully no one would ask where my parents were.

After a minute, Beryl appeared at the end of my row of chairs.

'Shall I sit with you today, my dear?' she asked. I smiled and nodded. Beryl shuffled to the seat next to mine and sat down with a happy sigh. I felt better, now Beryl was between me and everyone else.

'Well, I'm glad you're here, Nancy. I'm afraid we're a very small class today. Daniel and Aniela aren't very well, they've both caught a cold.'

'Oh ...'

'And Jake is with his mum, of course, with it being Mothering Sunday.'

The service began. We sang, and I joined in a little bit. After that, Paul said we were going to say thank you for our mothers, including those mothers who are no longer with us. I knew he was talking about all the old people's mothers who would have died, and also about Rob's mum. But it was true for me at that moment. In fact, when I looked around, the only person who seemed to have a mother with them was little Kim. It made me feel that we were all together, the oldest wrinkliest ladies in glasses and thick coats, and Beryl, and Rob, and me.

As I looked around the seats, everybody smiled.

I smiled back.

On Mother's Day, there are always little bunches of daffodils wrapped in silver foil. They are supposed to be for mothers, but there are always too many and the Sunday School children give them out to everyone.

Paul held two baskets full of daffodils, and wondered what to do.

'We haven't many children here today. Perhaps someone would like to give these out ...'

Kim's mum held her hand and walked to the front with her, and they took one basket.

I realised that after walking through the door on my own, this wouldn't be too scary. I stood up, walked to the front, and took the other basket. I gave bunches to everyone on my side of the church, and they were all so pleased in a way that I didn't mind at all. I took a bunch for my mum, and gave the basket back to Paul.

'Thank you for that, Nancy,' Paul said. He didn't say 'well done', as he probably would to a small child, and I sat down feeling calm and sensible and grown-up. It was a bit of a sad Mother's Day service, but I could still feel the rainbow inside. It had worked again.

We didn't go to our normal Sunday School room. Beryl, Paul, Kim and I went to the kitchen to make biscuits. I think this was supposed to be another present for our mothers, although Beryl didn't actually say that with Rob around. He didn't want to join in anyway. He sat on a cupboard in a corner playing on his PSP, and Beryl left him alone. I'm good at weighing flour and sugar and margarine, and I'm good at adding eggs bit by bit and beating them in.
Kim could help quite a lot too. We had a nice time.

'It's a shame Aniela and Daniel are poorly,' said Beryl. 'We were going to have a practice today for the holiday club drama.'

What *drama*? I glanced at Beryl, and she was looking at me, sideways, carefully.

'Aniela and Daniel's mum is organising a little play that the Sunday School are going to put on at Easter Club.'

I didn't say anything. You wouldn't exactly catch me being in a play that Magda was organising. We were quiet for a bit, then there was a voice from the cupboard in the corner.

'It's a stupid play,' said Rob. 'They call it a pantomime but they don't know what that is.'

'Now, Rob,' said Beryl. 'You know that the Kowalskis are learning a new language, and we know what they mean, don't we?'

Then we were quiet for a while.

'Is someone going to collect you when the service finishes?' Beryl asked me, when we'd put the biscuits in the oven.

I hadn't thought about that.

'I don't know' I answered.

She looked a little bit worried.

'Well, they know where you are, don't they?'

'Oh, yes,' I said.

I didn't know what would happen. My parents normally hang around for ages after church. I didn't have a key to get into our house. I would just have to stay at Biscuit Church for as long as I could. I could secretly wait in the boiler room, of course, but then I might get locked in when Paul went home ...

After Sunday School I went out to the foyer as usual. I was carrying my take-home sheet, my bunch of daffodils, and my paper bag of biscuits. There was no parent with a handbag to give them to. I put them all on a shelf and got my own chocolate biscuit. I stood and ate it. Everyone around me was talking to someone. If my mum and dad had been there, they would have been talking to someone too, but if I had nothing to do I could at least have stood next to one of them, or tried to pull their hand away while they tried to carry on talking.

At last, Paul found me and said he thought he could see my Dad's car outside. I gathered my daffodils and biscuits and went outside. He was right, the whole family were waiting there in the car. My parents were both smiling. My mum wound down the window.

'Come on love, let's go home.'

My fists tightened around the presents I was holding. Then I felt tears in my eyes. I held the cookie bag and daffodils through the open car window. My mum took them.

'Oh, thank you, Nancy. What's in here?'

Mum wasn't cross any more, but perhaps I was.

'I don't need a lift,' I stuttered, and turned towards the pedestrian crossing.

Sunday 25 March
Big Nancy

There was a piece of paper on the kitchen table. It had dropped through the door a couple of days ago. It was printed in the colours you get on a computer, with the name of our Biscuit Church and a little fish at the top. It said:

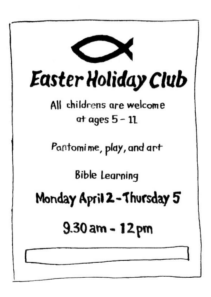

Easter Holiday Club

All childrens are welcome
at ages 5 – 11

Pantomime, play, and art

Bible Learning

Monday April 2 – Thursday 5

9.30 am – 12 pm

'Didn't they even get Paul to check this?' said my mum in her high voice. 'The English is all funny.

Would you send your child to that? No one's going to come.'

'Now, Nancy,' said Dad, changing the subject. 'What would you like to do today? Are you going to Biscuit Church on your own again, or coming to Jill's church with us?'

My mouth was full of cereal. While I chewed, Mum jumped in:

'You'd really like it, Nancy. There are so many girls your age, and there are a couple of families who I'm sure go to your school. And they don't just have biscuits, they have doughnuts, and Isaac really missed you last week, he just kept saying where's N–'

'I'm going to Biscuit Church,' I interrupted.

Mum took a deep breath, and turned to Dad.

'Mark, what's going to happen if we keep letting her do this? Don't you think she needs to take the plunge and get used to it?'

I looked at Dad.

'I don't know,' he said.

'You don't know? Well, this was your idea. I think you'd better work out what your plan is. We can't keep going to different churches. And we've been talking about going somewhere with more children for ages. *You* said it would be better for them.

But you didn't think it would be easy, did you, getting Nancy to do something different?'

'I don't know.'

'Stop saying you don't know!'

That was enough for me. I looked at the clock. It was a quarter to ten. Plenty of time. I went quietly upstairs while they carried on. I got dressed, washed my face, and brushed my teeth. I found a comb in my parents' room, and sorted my hair out. I sat on their bed and looked at myself in their big mirror. I could still hear their voices downstairs, not screaming this time, just rambling on in an argument that could never end. I looked at Mum's little alarm clock. Ten o'clock. Still too early. I picked up her big Bible again, and found my page.

Don't worry about anything; instead, pray about everything. Tell God what you need, and thank him for all he has done.

Oh. I'd better remember the thanking bit. I closed my eyes.

'Thank you for helping me last week. Thank you for helping me walk to church, and say hello, and give out daffodils.'

So what did I need today?

'I need my parents to come back to Hillytown Biscuit Church. I need my mum to be friends with Magda again, so I can be friends with Aniela.'

I opened my eyes and looked at the clock. Ten past ten. I crept downstairs. Mum and Dad were still at it, going on and on. I put my shoes on. I unbolted the front door, and opened it as quietly as I could. Just as I slipped out, Isaac appeared in the hall.

'Nancy!' he said.

'Bye, Isaac,' I whispered. And I was gone.

The sun was shining. There were more daffodils than last week. I took a deep breath, and as I breathed out, I felt bigger. I felt myself grow into the girl who went to church by herself, who helped Paul, who said hello. I walked with big steps, knowing exactly where I was going, singing to myself.

Suddenly, there were footsteps behind me, and panting, and a hand on my shoulder. I jumped.

'Aaah!'

It was my Dad.

'Nancy–' he panted. 'Nancy, you must never – never – ever – ever leave the house without telling us. I know we let you walk to church last week but ...'

'Sorry,' said big Nancy.

'It's OK,' said Dad. 'Nancy, you just said sorry!'

'I know', I said. 'When I go to church by myself I can say hello, and sorry, and I can talk to anybody.'

'Wow,' said Dad. 'Well done, Nancy. Well, if that's what happens, you'd better go!'

He smiled at me, and I looked at him.

'I'd rather you were all coming with me,' I said.

'Would you, Nancy?'

'I think Mum's just frightened of talking to Magda.'

'Well ...' Dad took a step back and scratched the back of his neck.

'You'd better be going,' I said.

'Will you be careful? We'll meet you after the service again.'

'OK. See you later!' big Nancy replied, and skipped off towards the main road.

Sunday 25 March
Mousie

When I got to church, there was Aniela in the foyer. She wasn't wearing her red velvet dress, she was dressed more like me, in a t-shirt and stretchy trousers. Her hair was in an enormous cascading ponytail. We hugged each other and then held hands and span around, getting in the way of the old people who were coming into church. Aniela took my hand and, before anyone could stop us we ran through the church,

through the dusty cupboard room, down the stairs, through the storeroom, and into the boiler room. Aniela turned the light on and began her spider check, holding me back at the door. What I saw, straight away, was the little mouse, standing on the floor, on his hind legs, looking straight at us. I turned Aniela's face towards mine. I put my finger on my lips and then slowly pointed.

'Ohhhhhh,' she sighed, reasonably quietly. We watched for a few seconds, and, amazingly, the mouse stayed still.

'Biscuit,' said Aniela, and she turned and disappeared back towards the stairs to fetch one. I crouched down very slowly, and then stayed completely still. Mousie dropped back onto four legs, and then began to scuttle around, doing mousey things like scratching his ear and washing his paws. I heard Aniela's footsteps, then, just when they got close, Mousie stood still, pricked up his ears, and shot off into a dark corner. Aniela had three whole chocolate digestives. I carefully put one just where Mousie had been standing. We ate the other two, and then, even though we hadn't heard the first song start, we set off back upstairs.

We ran into Magda.

I expected her to tell Aniela off about something. I

had forgotten, for the minute, that there was anything unusual about me for her to notice.

'Nancy, where are your mother and father?'

I stepped back. I twiddled my hair. I remembered that I was big Nancy.

'They're at a different church,' I said quietly.

'Excuse me, my dear, what did you say?' She leaned down to my level.

'They're at a different church,' I repeated, unable to make my voice any bigger.

'Oh ...' said Magda. A funny look came over her face. She stood up and looked at the windows. She looked pale.

'It's all right, I'm looking after Nancy.'

It was Beryl. I don't know if, or how, she knew what we were talking about, but I was glad she appeared. Aniela and I both went and sat with her for the first part of the service. This morning, Paul didn't appear on the stage. Instead, an older man climbed the steps to the old pulpit at the front of the church, and explained that Paul and Darek were both away at a conference. When he finished talking, the music group took over for singing. Aniela wanted me to read the words on the big screen to her. Even though everyone was singing them at the same time, I had to read them out loud, speaking into her ear. We sang one song where you sing one easy part over and over again, and after I'd read the words just once, she suddenly knew them, and sang along with everyone. I don't usually sing much in church, but once Aniela was singing, I joined in:

> *How great is our God*
> *Sing with me*
> *How great is our God*
> *All will see*
> *How great, how great, is our God.* *

The next time round, Aniela did the 'sing with me', and I did the 'all will see', which sounded really good. It made us laugh too. It was funny because we normally still talked to each other one word at a time, and here we were, singing together like girls in a band.

Eventually, we went upstairs for Sunday School. There was me, Aniela, Daniel, Jake, Rob and Kim. There was also a visitor.

Magda.

We all sat down on the tiny chairs, and she sat down too, pulling her straight skirt around her knees.

'We must rehearse pantomime for the Easter Club,' Magda announced. 'We have missed one week

---

*From 'The splendour of the king' by Chris Tomlin, Jesse Reeves, and Ed Cash © 2004.

86

already and there is one more Sunday before the club begins. Here are your words.'

She gave everyone a photocopied sheet. 'What about singing?' asked Rob, guitar ready as always.

Beryl looked at Magda. 'Perhaps ... perhaps we could have a little song first?'

'Perhaps we should look at the pantomime first,' Magda replied.

I looked at my sheet. At the top it said 'The Parable of the Lost Sheep'. Next to it was my name, written by hand, and 'Lost Sheep' in capitals.

'Nancy, I have given you the part of lost sheep, as you do not like to speak. You will ... you will be at Easter Club?'

I felt my face go red, for more than one reason. But it hadn't occurred to me that I wouldn't be at Easter Club, not for a minute, so I just nodded, without thinking. Did that mean I'd said yes to being in the play?

'Your brother can be sheep also, with Kim. Let's begin.'

'Her brother isn't allowed to come without one of his parents,' muttered Rob.

'Excuse me?' said Magda.

'I said, Isaac can't come without one of his parents. He's under five,' Rob repeated, a bit louder.

Magda made a noise like 'Der ...' and stopped dead.

'Let's not worry about that now, Rob,' said Beryl, in rescuing mode again. 'Shall we read through our lines? Then perhaps we can do something more–'

'Aniela will begin,' Magda announced.

Aniela was studying her script very closely. I looked at mine. The first line said 'narrator' and there was quite a lot to read. We waited while Aniela found her place with her finger. Kim fidgeted on her chair.

'Wonk,' said Aniela. There were giggles.

I looked at the script. '*Once* ,' I whispered.

'Once,' said Aniela.

Kim slid off her chair.

'*Upon,*' I whispered.

'Upon,' Aniela repeated. 'A,' she continued, a bit pleased with herself.

'*Time.*'

'Time.'

'There was a farmer who had a hundred sheep,' Jake read. 'Yeah, yeah, can we get on with it?'

'Now, Jake, Aniela is just learning,' said Beryl. 'Kim, can you sit on your chair, darling?'

'Aniela will learn words,' said Magda. 'Rob, it is your part.'

Rob sighed and shuffled.

'I am a farmer with a hundred sheep,' he mumbled. 'This is my apprentice, Jake.'

'Have you counted the sheep today, Master?' Jake mumbled back.

'No, young Jake, I thought you had counted the sheep. Let us count them together.'

'One, two, miss a few, ninety-nine, a hundred.'

'No, no, no!' said Magda.

'This is boring,' Jake moaned. 'We should do that thing again where the girls fall in the water.

That was funny. That would be *entertainment*!'

'Come on!' said Rob. 'Let's start again. Wonk upon a time ...'

I started to giggle. Aniela giggled too.

'When are we going to do singing?' said Kim.

'Sshh,' said Beryl.

'What's Daniel doing in this?' Rob asked.

'Daniel will play keyboard,' Magda replied. 'He is very good at playing music to accompany the panto-mime. But keyboard is in church today so he can't practise.'

''Snot fair,' Rob muttered, letting his hand drop and strum the guitar.

Bored, I whispered to Aniela, 'Snot!'

'Wonk!' she whispered back. Then we couldn't stop giggling. Magda tried to tell us to carry on, Beryl tried to persuade us to get it done quickly. Slowly, we made our way through the play. All I had to do was wander off while Rob and Jake were counting to a hundred, and then later Rob would come and find me. We were just reading the play, not acting out, so today I didn't have to do anything at all. Jake kept asking questions, Rob kept mumbling. Magda started to get all uptight, and took it out on Aniela, who was still giggling with me. Daniel just slouched, almost a straight line from head to foot, on his tiny chair, staring at the ceiling. In the end, Beryl suggested that we leave the rehearsing and use the time to make sheep costumes. Magda had had enough and let us get white card and cotton wool out. But after the cotton wool had got everywhere, and before we'd worked out how to make a sheep costume out of it, we heard the last song finish downstairs, and it was biscuit time.

Sunday 25 March
The Flood

Aniela and I wanted to check on Mousie again. We could do that before Magda might worry that we were in the boiler room. We took three biscuits again, and ran to the basement steps. We are definitely the fastest. Daniel and Jake had only just got down the Sunday School steps, and they saw us run past. 'Hey, where are you going?' Jake called. Then Daniel called out in Polish. We ignored them and ran through the playgroup storeroom, but when we stopped at the boiler room door for a spider *and* mouse check, we heard foot-steps, and then the boys caught up with us.

'What're you doing in here?' Jake asked.

'Bringing food for our mouse,' I replied.

They seemed impressed, but rather than crouch-ing and waiting, they put the light on, barged in, and started looking around in all the corners.

'There's no mouse in here' Jake sneered.

'Just many big *spiders*,' said Daniel, and quickly translated in case his sister didn't get it. Aniela kicked out at Daniel. He pushed her back.

'There aren't any spiders. We've checked,' I said. 'And there is a mouse, you're just being far too noisy for him.'

Without really thinking, I grabbed hold of the pipe that goes across the room and somersaulted over it again.

'Hey, move over,' said Jake, and did the same thing. Then Daniel had a go. Then Aniela, but she got stuck just as she had before.

'Look at this!' Jake called. He had jumped up and grabbed a higher pipe, and was swinging by his arms. I couldn't resist that. I jumped up next to him and swung. I could swing further and I could swing for longer. Until Daniel pushed me out of the way. There was another pipe, even higher up. I climbed onto the boiler itself, and from there I could reach it. The pipe was a bit hot, so I didn't swing for long. Perhaps we should stop, before someone got burned or something got broken. Then I heard an 'aaaahhhhh!' sound behind me.

Aniela had climbed onto the first pipe, the one we had somersaulted over, and she was standing on it, balanced on her hands and feet like a monkey. Suddenly, something moved, and Aniela's whole body swung right round and fell with a thud onto the concrete. She screamed, and I jumped in to move her away, because the pipe she had been balancing on had come loose at one of its joints, and there was water, hot water, pouring down onto the floor.

We pulled Aniela to the raised bit of the floor and I sat with my arm on her back, rubbing it like my mum does. Thankfully, she hadn't got too wet or scalded. Still, Aniela cried and cried. Daniel looked at her eyes, and made sure she could move her fingers and toes, and talked to her much more kindly in Polish. Then he looked at the broken pipe.

'We've got to fix this.'

I jumped up and grabbed the tea towel that had

hung in one place for five years, and sort of wound it round the split pipe so that it pulled both ends together. I wound it round again and tied a knot.

'Good job,' said Jake.

'Now,' said Daniel. 'Aniela. Jake. Nancy. Listen to me.' He drew us together into a huddle and looked into each of our eyes in turn.

'We will not tell anyone of this. We will not tell anyone we were here. Do you understand?'

'What about the leak?' I said.

'It will not make a difference. The church will mend the pipe anyway. It will make no difference except to us if they know we were here.'

'But will they find out soon enough?' I asked. I could see the tea towel was already soaked and dripping.

'Of course they will know. It will be fine. Just say nothing.'

'It was you who started it,' said Jake.

'If my mother would learn that you started this, she will not allow you to be friends with Aniela. So be quiet, OK?'

Aniela sobbed again. I nodded.

'So let's go,' said Daniel.

I took Aniela to the ladies' toilet so she could wash

her face and dry her clothes a bit. I looked at her poor back too, where there was going to be a nasty bruise. How was she going to explain that to her mum?

Aniela put her arms around my neck.

'Best friend?' she asked.

'Best friend,' I replied. Aniela smiled a little, and she was ready to go back upstairs.

Magda had just started looking for Daniel and Aniela, and they set off pretty quickly. There were a few people still chatting in the church and in the foyer. I got another biscuit and hung around. Mum and Dad might already be waiting in the car, but I didn't feel good about the boiler room. Paul was away, Darek was away, how long might it be before anyone went in there? Perhaps I should just check it again before I went home.

Down in the basement, the tea towel seemed to be doing no good at all. Water was just pouring down it onto the lower part of the floor, which had become a shallow pool. And the whole room was full of steam. I couldn't leave this. I didn't want to tell anyone. But what could I do? I looked quickly around the playgroup storeroom. Painting aprons. I grabbed a plastic painting apron and tried to reach the broken pipe. I could throw the apron over the join, but I couldn't wrap it tightly. If I could get closer I could tie the apron strings. That might just slow the flood down. I felt the water. It wasn't too hot, once it had hit the cold concrete floor. I quickly took my shoes and socks off. rolled my trousers up, and stepped in, and tried to tie the apron to the pipe. So much for my feet, it was my top that got all wet doing this. It didn't do a lot of good – I couldn't make the strings work properly. Back in the storeroom, I found a roll of sticky tape. Back into the water. Pull, roll, pull, roll. I'm no good at biting sticky tape so I left the roll hanging there.

I stood back. There were only drips now. Of course the broken pipe, the tea towel, the apron, and the roll of sticky tape looked suspicious, to say the least. But the most important thing was to save Hillytown Biscuit Church from flooding.

I picked up my shoes and socks, and tiptoed to the ladies' toilets, where I could get my feet dry. As I dried my toes with paper towels, I noticed that it was quiet. No talking. No footsteps. I put my socks and shoes on, and went back to the dusty cupboard room. The door that goes into church was shut. And it was locked. I listened. There wasn't a sound. A horrible feeling fluttered inside me.

I ran back through the dusty cupboard room, and

into the back hall. No one there. I ran upstairs to Sunday School. No one in there. I tried the side door that goes onto the street. It was locked.

Everyone had gone.

I looked for windows. There are windows that open in the back hall, but they are very high up. I pushed a table to the wall, and put a chair on top of it, and climbed up carefully. It was scary because I was shaking. I tried to pull at the window. It wouldn't move, and my chair wobbled. What was I thinking, anyway? How would I get down from that height outside? I needed to be lower down.

Back to the basement. There are windows down there. They are high up on the basement walls, but they are right next to the ground outside. I climbed on a playgroup cupboard. This was wobbly too, it was on wheels. There was one bit of window that looked as though it should open, but the metal bits had rusted into place and there was no way it would move. I tried the same thing in the boiler room, where the drip had turned back into a stream. I climbed down and sat on the old chair I had used to reach the window. It was hopeless. No one knew I was here. My parents may have waited outside, but they would soon have driven home to see if I'd gone there. Everyone at church would assume I'd gone. There was no way out, and the flood was getting worse. I put my head in my hands and made a sobbing noise. But I didn't feel like crying.

I opened my eyes, and saw a tiny pair of black eyes looking back at me. Mousie was at the edge of the room, higher up than the water and safe.

'Hello,' I whispered. 'What should I do, Mousie?'

Mousie carried on looking, absolutely still. Of course I knew what to do. I closed my eyes.

'Dear God,' I prayed. 'I need to get out of this building and stop this flood. Please help me.' God hadn't sorted out the last thing yet, about my family going back to Hillytown, but this was more urgent.

When I opened my eyes, Mousie had vanished. Then I noticed a funny little metal door on the wall in front of me. I remembered something about this door. It was something about Easter Club last year. My mum had come down here before the club start-

ed, to get a key to open Paul's office, where all her tuck shop things were.

I opened the door. There was the key. I ran upstairs, not sure what the windows in Paul's office were like, but it was worth a try. The key worked, and I got in. Before I even looked at the windows, however, I saw something else on Paul's desk.

A phone.

Sunday 25 March
The Phone

I felt sick.

I have never used a phone.

Well, I have listened quietly while my grandma said 'Happy Birthday'. That is all. Phones make me feel sick.

So I've never phoned my parents. I do know their number, though. It's 875 8925.

I had to do it. I had to do it. It was one of those phones with a coily wire. I picked it up.

It went 'brrrrrrr'.

I whispered 'Help me, God.'

I pressed the buttons. 875, 8925.

The phone played a little tune back to me. Then it was quiet. Then it rang. My stomach churned.

It carried on ringing. Then it clicked. Then I heard my mum saying 'Please leave a message for Mark, Rachel, Nancy or Isaac, after the tone.' Then it beeped.

'Mum?' I said quietly. 'Mum, Dad, I'm stuck at church. You'll need to get a key to get me out.'

Then I put the phone down. Where were they? Were they still outside? How late was it?

I wondered how they'd get in, anyway. Paul had a key, of course, but he was away. Rob was staying at Beryl's house. Maybe she had a key.

Then I noticed something. Next to the phone, on the desk, was a little sticky note. It said 'Darek 822 4035'. Darek would have a key. He was away too, but his key probably wasn't with him. Perhaps Magda could find it.

I had felt sick just phoning my own house. Now I was thinking about phoning *Magda*. Even if I didn't mind phoning her, Daniel would still kill me when she found out about the boiler room. But I had to do it. I had to do it.

I took a deep breath.

'*Please* help me, God,' I whispered. I picked up the phone and dialled. 822, 4035. Little tune. Quiet. Ring ring. Ring ring.

'Hello, Kowalski family? Hello, here is Magda Kowalski. Hello, who is there?'

I put the phone down. I needed to find my words. I needed to get them all the way from my churning stomach to my mouth.

'Please God, I need to speak to Magda!' I whispered, with no sound at all coming out.

822 4035. Little tune. Quiet. Ring ring. Ring ring.

'Hello, Magda Kowalski.'

'Hello.'

'Hello, who is there?'

'Nancy.'

'Excuse me? Nancy? *Nancy*!'

'I'm locked in at church. Have you got a key?'

'You are ... oh ...'

'Can you come?'

'Oh my poor child! Oh dear! Oh, I'm afraid I am not able to drive, my child. Where are your parents?'

I explained that they weren't in when I rang them. Magda said not to worry, she would find them, and someone would be there very soon to let me out.

I just couldn't leave it there.

'Magda,' I said, feeling, for the first time, that she might be my friend. 'There's something else. There's a problem with the boiler. There's a bit of a flood. Which is ... it's my fault. But you need to send someone who can do something about it.'

'Oh,' said Magda, a bit confused. 'Oh, yes, do not worry, my dear, we will sort everything out.'

I put the phone down, and flopped, shaking, and hugely relieved, into Paul's comfy armchair.

I didn't have much time there before the phone rang. Of course, I'd never answered a phone before, but I did now, and it was my hysterical mum. As she gradually calmed down, I managed to explain everything, and that it was no good contacting Paul, she needed to drive to Magda's flat and get the church key. She explained that they had been late getting back for me, and the church had been closed, and then I wasn't at home, so they'd driven around a bit, to friends' houses and the playground, thinking I would have gone somewhere like that. They had already tried Paul, and they had actually spoken to Beryl, but of course she didn't know where I was. I told her about the pipe, and I said again that it was my fault, before she started talking to Magda. Mum just said the same thing: 'Don't worry, we'll be there as soon as we can.'

About ten minutes later, there was a knock on the side door. I ran over there, and heard my dad's voice. He pushed open the letterbox and talked to me through it. He'd walked up with Isaac while Mum went for the key in the car. I told him about the boiler, and he said there would be a tap somewhere that would turn the water off, but I'd better wait now until the grown-ups got in.

'That was very brave of you, to phone the Kowalskis,' he said.

'I know,' I said. 'But God helped me.'

'Really?' said Dad. 'Well, your mum's being very brave right now, driving over there and talking to Magda. Perhaps he'll help her too.'

'He will if she asks,' I said.

'Yes, but we could ask too.'

'OK.'

'Shall I? Dear God, please help Mum to be brave about talking to Magda again.'

'And please help them to agree with each other,' I added.

'Amen,' said Dad. 'Amen.'

When our car arrived, it contained Mum, Magda, Daniel, Aniela, and a set of keys. They all came in, and we all went down to the basement. The flood hadn't really got any worse. Magda said, 'I have told my children to never play in here, it is not safe.'

Daniel and Aniela both looked at me. They looked a bit scared.

'I'm sorry,' I said in a little voice. 'It's all my fault'.

I sort of collapsed in the direction of Mum. She caught me and we hugged. It's not something we do so much these days. It made me cry a bit.

'I don't think you'll do that again now, will you?' said Mum.

'Errr ...' Daniel started. Everyone looked at him.

'We ...' said Aniela. She couldn't find the right word.

'It was not only Nancy,' Daniel agreed. 'It was all of us. We were all climbing.'

'Sorry,' said Aniela.

'Sorry,' said Daniel.

'Well,' said Mum. 'Your mother and I have been saying sorry too. I think we've had enough sorrys now, we need a cup of tea.'

Dad phoned someone called Pete who looks after

the church heating, and we all stayed to let him in when he arrived. The parents made tea, we raided the biscuits, and we all sat in Paul's office, just like we did on the spider day.

'Have you eaten lunch?' Mum asked, as Daniel and Aniela pleaded for another biscuit.

'No,' said Magda. 'We are all very hungry'.

'I've got a chicken in the oven,' said Mum. 'I'm sure it will do for all of us. Why don't you come over for lunch after Pete gets here?'

'Yessss!' cried Aniela.

We had a great time that afternoon. Daniel and Aniela just thought it was wonderful to have a *garden*. They've never had one, here or in Poland. We have a climbing frame and a trampoline in ours, and we just bounced and climbed while my parents got the food ready, and then climbed and bounced for hours afterwards. The grown-ups were inside talking and talking about the Easter Club drama. Mum had some ideas about making it more fun, and in the end she dragged us inside to see what we thought. She thought that Aniela would make an excellent sheep, rather than a narrator.

'She could be a singing sheep,' I suggested.

'Who's playing the shepherd?' Mum asked.

'Rob,' said Magda. 'But he does not want to at all. He just wants to play music all the time.'

'But shepherds do play music,' said Mum. 'He could play his guitar for the sheep.'

They went on, talking, and writing, and asking us what we thought, for ages and ages. We went in and out, and bounced, and climbed, and played hide and seek, until it started to get dark. We all decided to ask Jake's dad and Kim's mum if we could meet to practise after church next week, so that we didn't have to miss another Sunday School. That would be the

day before Easter Club began. My mum and Magda talked about cooking pizzas in the church kitchen, so the Sunday School children could all have lunch together.

That meant my family was coming to Biscuit Church next week. Brilliant. Thank you, God, I whispered. Thank you, thank you, thank you.

Our play was the first thing on the first morning of Easter Club. We were going to do the play, then sing some songs, Paul was going to talk a little bit, and then everyone was going to make sheep with cotton wool and pipe cleaners, before we had a tuck shop and some silly games.

'How do we get the drinks and biscuits from Paul's office?' Magda called. 'It's locked, I don't have the key'

'I know!' I said, and shot downstairs, my sheep's tail flying behind me. I ran into the boiler room, glanced at the mended pipe, which looked as good as new, grabbed the key from inside the little door, and ran back upstairs. When I got there, Paul was already opening the door. He saw the key I was holding.

'Oh, yes, Nancy, I heard you found my secret key! Very resourceful.'

'I'm sorry.'

'No, don't be silly, it's not really secret!'

'I mean ... I'm sorry about the broken pipe.'

He stopped what he was doing. 'Nancy,' he said, a bit seriously now. 'You helped to mend something far more important than a pipe. I want to say thank you for that.'

I *thought* I knew what he was talking about. It was a nice thing to say, anyway. I helped him carry the tuck shop things into the back hall, and then I took the key back to its hiding place. Pausing for just a couple of seconds to hear the boiler room drips, I said thank you to God for answering all my requests. Then I asked him to help me with what I had to do next.

We put on our sheep tunics and sheep hats, all made out of white card and cotton wool, and waited outside the main church room. The feeling I had in my tummy today was sort of fluttery. I was scared, but I was a bit excited too. It seemed pretty noisy in there.

'Everybody here?' asked Mum.

I looked around. 'We're all here.'

We opened the door, and went in.

The church was full! There were children on every row of seats. Some I knew from school, some I knew from things like swimming lessons, some I'd never seen before. They weren't still or quiet, they seemed to be raring to get up and do something. But when they saw us dressed in sheep suits and tea towels, they

laughed, and we had their attention. We sheep arranged ourselves on the steps of the old pulpit, Aniela at the very top. My mum picked up a microphone and welcomed all the children.

'And now' she announced, 'may I introduce to you: Shepherd Boyz with Lambiella!'

'Hang on, hang on,' said Rob. 'We need to count the sheep first!'

'Yes, master!' said Jake. He scanned the pulpit, 'One, two, miss a few, ninety-nine, a hundred!'

'Are you sure?' said Rob, and Jake did it again.

'One, two, miss a few, ninety-nine, a hundred!'

'OK, then we can begin!'

Rob sat down with his guitar. He had spent a lot of time teaching Jake this song. Daniel played keyboards. It was a song about a shepherd. The sheep joined in with baas, except for Aniela, who had her own special part in the chorus, singing different notes from Rob and Jake. She was brilliant. Her voice filled the church, the children listening mostly went quiet, and I was so proud she was my friend. The chorus goes like this:

> *I will trust in you alone*
> *I will trust in you alone*

For your endless mercy follows me
*Your goodness will lead me home. *

I had a different job to do. While they were singing, I had to sneak out of the pulpit and get lost. In the rehearsals, I'd just walked to the back of the church, but now I had a better idea. I got down on all fours and began to crawl, looking up every now and again to go 'baa!' I crawled off the stage and down one of the aisles. Then I turned into one of the rows of seats and crawled over feet to the other end. Somehow, I was being so silly I didn't feel shy at all, and saying baa is different from saying words. Every time I looked up and said baa! everyone around me laughed.

By the end of the song I'd crawled through several rows of children and found a place to crouch out of sight. I couldn't stop giggling. Jake counted the sheep again – 'One, two, miss a few, ninety-nine … Uh-oh ...'

In the story, the shepherd realises that one sheep is missing, and then spends all day looking for it. Rob climbed up and down the pulpit steps, pretending it was a mountain, and through the microphones, as if they were a forest. He started asking the audience if they'd seen a sheep. They were joining in now. They

_____

*From 'The Lord's my shepherd' by Stuart Townsend © 1996.

kept me well hidden. They let me scuttle about under the chairs to get away from Rob. For a while, I think he really couldn't see me. But the screams from some girls from my school, when I appeared under their chairs, finally gave me away.

Rob made his way along the row of chairs, calling 'stop that sheep!' Then he did something I didn't expect at all.

He reached down, grabbed me around the waist, which tickled and made me laugh, picked me up, and put me over his shoulder. He carried me, red faced and hysterical, back along the row, and down the aisle to the stage. I was laughing so much I couldn't breathe. And so was the audience.

'I've found my sheep!' Rob cried. 'It's time for a party!'

Mum turned on two sets of disco lights, and Daniel, still in his sheep costume, started a disco beat on his keyboard and began to play. We all danced on the stage, which I would never have done, but Aniela was holding my hands. Even Magda and my mum jumped on the stage and danced a bit. Then Daniel brought the music to a close and we all stood together and bowed while the audience clapped. Aniela squeezed my hand. I looked out at the sea of faces. Our church was full of children!

The question was, would there ever be enough biscuits?